WHO DO YOU THINK YOU ARE?

A
Family
HISTORY

Photographs & Memories

Who do you think you are? A *Family* History

Photographs & Memories

Photographs & Memories

The Marriage

....

and

....

were joined together in marriage on

....

at

....

This edition © Robert Frederick Ltd. 2007
4 North Parade, Bath, U.K. BA1 1LF

Printed in China

CONTENTS

❖ The Marriage 8

❖ Tracing Your Family History 16

❖ Husband's Genealogy 20

❖ Wife's Genealogy 22

❖ Our Children 26

❖ Our Grandchildren 32

❖ Our Great Grandchildren 40

❖ Husband's Ancestral Chart 42

❖ Wife's Ancestral Chart 46

❖ Weddings 50

❖ Religious Ceremonies 58

❖ Education 62

❖ Family Homes 66

❖ Family Vehicles 70

❖ Family Pets 74

❖ Events to Remember 78

❖ Reunions 82

❖ Family Holidays 86

❖ Illnesses 94

❖ Clubs & Organisations 98

❖ Family Friends 102

❖ Family Hobbies 108

❖ Family Sports 112

❖ Family Collections 116

with quotations and woodcuts throughout,
and pages for Notes and Photographs

Family Tree - Inside Front and Inside Back Covers

Family Notes

Family Notes

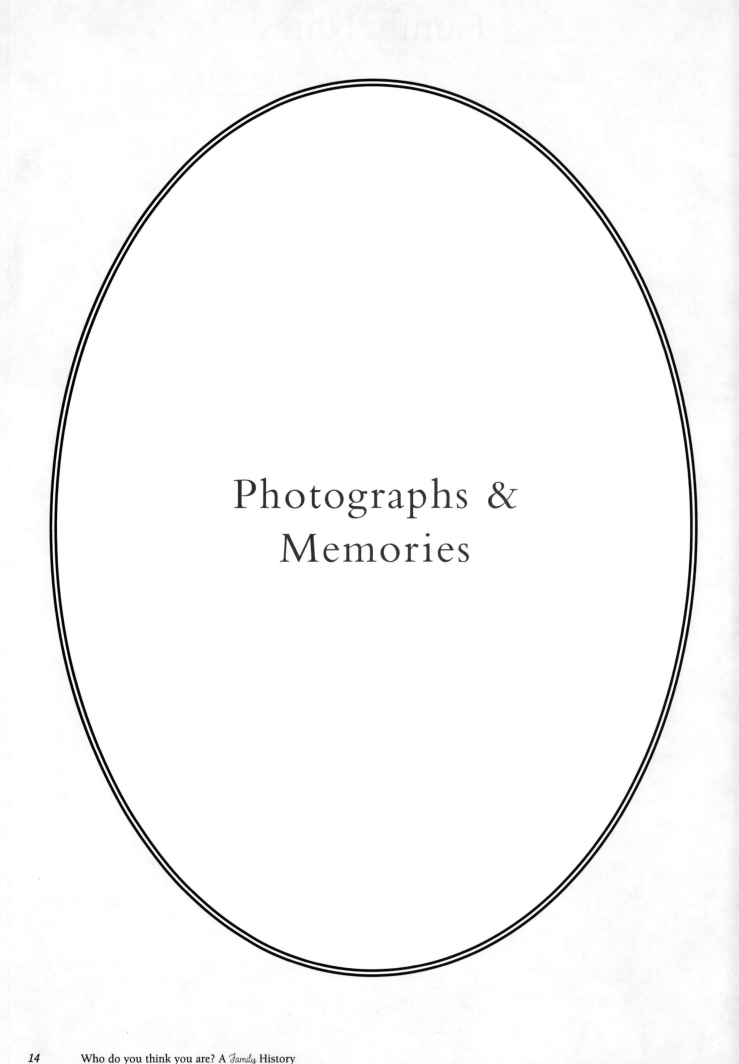

Photographs & Memories

A Family History

Have you ever thought about who your ancestors were? – what they did, what they achieved, where they came from? Well, if so, this book is for you. Designed to keep forever a record of your family history, it also gives valuable information and useful hints as to how to go about your research.

From the youngest child just born to your great great grandparents, this book gives you a unique opportunity to learn more about the origins of your family. More than anything, this is a book about people, not just names, dates and places.

We sincerely hope that you enjoy compiling your family history. When complete, it will provide a treasure-trove of information, achievements and memories, and will be a wonderful gift for your children and grandchildren And maybe you can even learn more about yourself from studying your ancestors.
For as Walt Whitman once wrote:

"The Past! The dark unfathom'd retrospect!
The teeming gulf! The sleepers and the shadows!
The past! The infinite greatness of the past!
For what is the present after all,
but a growth out of the past?"

Tracing Your Family History

Here are some useful hints to help you
trace your family tree.

1. LIVING RELATIVES

First-hand information is always the best. Your elderly relatives should be able to give you much information about their own families, their parents and grandparents, where they lived, what jobs they did and so on. Make a list of as many names as possible. They may have hoarded old documents, certificates and family photographs which will help you in your investigation.

2. OFFICIAL RECORDS

General Register Office

The General Register Office, P.O.Box 2, Southport PR8 2JD, holds records dating back to 1st July 1837 for England and Wales. (www.gro.gov.uk). There is no charge for searching the indexes. You can request a copy of your own birth certificate, and from this you can work backwards, looking for both your parents' birth and marriage certificates, the marriage certificates of both sets of grandparents and so on. Once the entry has been found a full certificate can be supplied for a small fee.

Scottish Record Office

If you were born in Scotland you will need to consult the Scottish Record Office, New Register House, 3 West Register Street, Edinburgh EH1 3YT. (www.gro-scotland.gov.uk)

Australia/New Zealand Record Office

In Australia, births, deaths and marriages are governed separately by state legislation. The following site provides links to each state registry - www.australia.gov.au/419

In New Zealand, this information can be found at - www.bdm.govt.nz

Local Parish Registers

For records of births, marriages and deaths before 1837 you will need to consult local parish registers which were first ordered to be kept in 1538. Not all parish registers have survived and many did not begin until the late 1600's. Most registers existing are in the hands of the clergy or locked for safe-keeping in the County or Diocesan Record Offices. Consulting these can be a lengthy process, especially in the larger cities, or if your families moved around the country a lot. However, there are some short-cuts. Phillimore and Co Ltd (Shopwyke Manor Barn, Chichester, West Sussex PO20 2BG) have published hundreds of parish registers thus minimizing the necessity for travelling all over the country. The Society of Genealogists (14 Charterhouse Buildings, Goswell Road, London EC1M 7BA) also hold many copies.

To trace your ancestors you will thus need to know which parish they were born in. You can search for this in the census returns.

3. CENSUS

A census has been taken every 10 years from 1801 and returns for 1841, 1851 and 1861 are housed in the Public Records Office (The National Archives, Kew, Richmond, Surrey TW9 4DU) and can be inspected by the general public. The census return gives information as to where each person was born, indicating which parish registers should be targeted for your searches.

4. OTHER DENOMINATIONS

Parish registers did not cover Dissentors, Foreigners and Jews. Sources for these groups can be found in the 12 volume National Index of Parish Registers published by Phillimore & Co. The Index includes records for the following groups: Nonconformists, Presbyterians, Independents, Baptists, Society of Friends, Moravians, Methodists, Foreign Churches, Roman Catholics and for Jewish Genealogy.

We wish you every success in your endeavour to trace your ancestors.

"To be able to enjoy one's past life is to live twice."

MARTIAL

Photographs & Memories

 A *Family* History

"To forget one's ancestors is to be a brook without a source,
a tree without a root."
CHINESE PROVERB

A history of the .... family

19

Husband's Genealogy

Record information about his family.

Husband's Full Name   _____

Birth Date   _____

Birth Place   _____

Father's Full Name   _____

Mother's Full Name   _____

Brothers & Sisters

"An ideal wife is any
woman who has an
ideal husband."
BOOTH TARKINGTON

Wife's Genealogy

Record information about her family.

Wife's Full Name   --

Birth Date   --

Birth Place   --

Father's Full Name   --

Mother's Full Name   --

Brothers & Sisters

_____

_____

_____

_____

_____

_____

Family Notes

Family Notes

Our Children

Full Name

Date of Birth

Place of Birth

Weight

~

Full Name

Date of Birth

Place of Birth

Weight

~

Full Name

Date of Birth

Place of Birth

Weight

Our Children

Full Name

_____

_____

Date of Birth

_____

Place of Birth

_____

Weight

_____

"Children are the true connoisseurs.
What's precious to them has no price, only value."
BEL KAUFMAN

Our Children

Full Name

Date of Birth

Place of Birth

Weight

~

Full Name

Date of Birth

Place of Birth

Weight

~

Full Name

Date of Birth

Place of Birth

Weight

Our Children

Full Name

Date of Birth

Place of Birth

Weight

~

Full Name

Date of Birth

Place of Birth

Weight

~

Full Name

Date of Birth

Place of Birth

Weight

Photographs & Memories

Photographs & Memories

Our Grandchildren

Full Name

Date of Birth

Place of Birth

Weight

~

Full Name

Date of Birth

Place of Birth

Weight

~

Full Name

Date of Birth

Place of Birth

Weight

Our Grandchildren

Full Name

Date of Birth

Place of Birth

Weight

Our Grandchildren

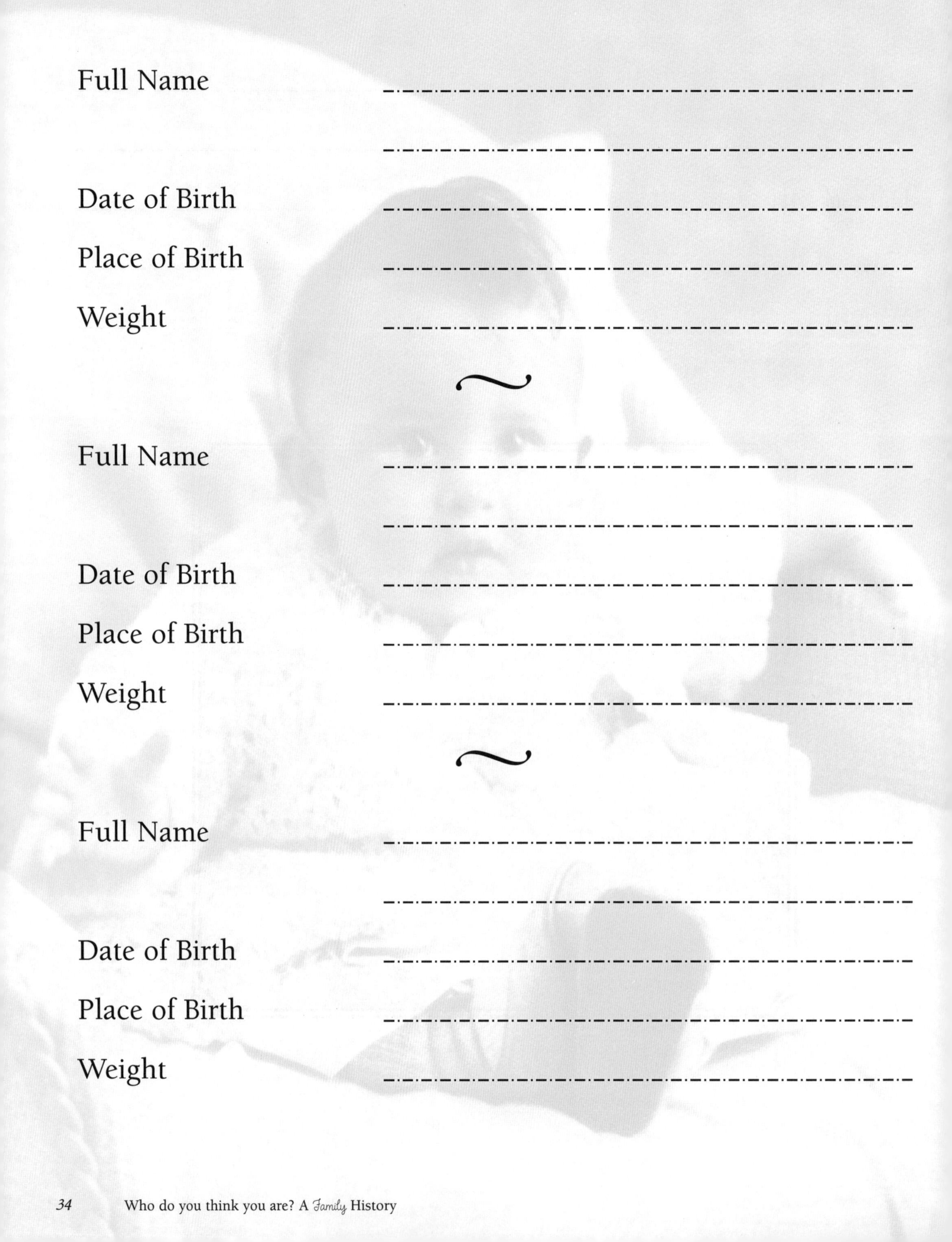

Full Name

_____

_____

Date of Birth

_____

Place of Birth

_____

Weight

_____

~

Full Name

_____

_____

Date of Birth

_____

Place of Birth

_____

Weight

_____

~

Full Name

_____

_____

Date of Birth

_____

Place of Birth

_____

Weight

_____

Our Grandchildren

Full Name

Date of Birth

Place of Birth

Weight

~

Full Name

Date of Birth

Place of Birth

Weight

~

Full Name

Date of Birth

Place of Birth

Weight

Our Grandchildren

Full Name

Date of Birth

Place of Birth

Weight

~

Full Name

Date of Birth

Place of Birth

Weight

~

Full Name

Date of Birth

Place of Birth

Weight

Our Grandchildren

Full Name

Date of Birth

Place of Birth

Weight

~

Full Name

Date of Birth

Place of Birth

Weight

~

Full Name

Date of Birth

Place of Birth

Weight

Photographs & Memories

Who do you think you are? A *Family* History

Photographs &
Memories

Our Great Grandchildren

Full Name _____

_____

Date of Birth _____

Place of Birth _____

Weight _____

~

Full Name _____

_____

Date of Birth _____

Place of Birth _____

Weight _____

~

Full Name _____

_____

Date of Birth _____

Place of Birth _____

Weight _____

Our Great Grandchildren

Full Name --

Date of Birth --

Place of Birth --

Weight --

Full Name --

Date of Birth --

Place of Birth --

Weight --

"In a brief space the generations of beings are changed, runners, pass on the torches of life."
LUCRETIUS

Husband's Ancestral Chart

Father's Name

Date of Birth _____ Died _____

Place of Birth _____

Notes _____

Husband

Mother's Nam

Date _____ Died _____

_____ Birth _____

_____ces _____

"A people without history is like wind on the buffalo grass."
SIOUX PROVERB

Great Grandfather's Name

Grandfather's Name

Date of Birth _____ Died _____

Place of Birth _____

Great Grandmother's Name

Great Grandfather's Name

Grandmother's Name

Date of Birth _____ Died _____

Place of Birth _____

Great Grandmother's Name

Great Grandfather's Name

Grandfather's Name

Date of Birth _____ Died _____

Place of Birth _____

Great Grandmother's Name

Great Grandfather's Name

Grandmother's Name

Date of Birth _____ Died _____

Place of Birth _____

Great Grandmother's Name

Great Great Grandfather's Name

Great Great Grandmother's Name

Great Great Grandfather's Name

Great Great Grandmother's Name

Great Great Grandfather's Name

Great Great Grandmother's Name

Great Great Grandfather's Name

Great Great Grandmother's Name

Great Great Grandfather's Name

Great Great Grandmother's Name

Great Great Grandfather's Name

Great Great Grandmother's Name

Great Great Grandfather's Name

Great Great Grandmother's Name

Great Great Grandfather's Name

Great Great Grandmother's Name

Great Great Grandparents

Great Great Great Grandparents

Family Notes

What do you know about your ancestors?
When were they alive? Did they have special interests,
hobbies, skills or perhaps unusual characteristics?
Ask older family members what they remember about
past family members.

Wife's Ancestral Chart

Father's Name _____

Date of Birth _____ Died _____

Place of Birth _____

Notes _____

_____

Wife _____

Mother's Name _____

Date of Birth _____ Died _____

Place of Birth _____

Notes _____

"Remember me when
I am gone away,
Gone far away into the silent land."
CHRISTINA ROSSETTI

Great Grandfather's Name

Grandfather's Name

Date of Birth _____ Died _____

Great Grandmother's Name

Grandmother's Name

Date of Birth _____ Died _____

Place of Birth _____

Great Grandfather's Name

Great Grandmother's Name

Great Grandfather's Name

Grandfather's Name

Date of Birth _____ Died _____

Place of Birth _____

Great Grandmother's Name

Grandmother's Name

Date of Birth _____ Died _____

Place of Birth _____

Great Grandfather's Name

Great Grandmother's Name

Great Great Grandfather's Name

Great Great Grandmother's Name

Great Great Grandfather's Name

Great Great Grandmother's Name

Great Great Grandfather's Name

Great Great Grandmother's Name

Great Great Grandfather's Name

Great Great Grandmother's Name

Great Great Grandfather's Name

Great Great Grandmother's Name

Great Great Grandfather's Name

Great Great Grandmother's Name

Great Great Grandfather's Name

Great Great Grandmother's Name

Great Great Grandparents   Great Great Great Grandparents

Family Notes

What do you know about your ancestors?
When were they alive? Did they have special interests,
hobbies, skills or perhaps unusual characteristics?
Ask older family members what they remember about
past family members.

Weddings

Write about family weddings here. What did the bride wear?
Where did the couple go on their honeymoon?

Bride ....

Groom ....

Date ....

Bridesmaids / Matron of Honour

....

....

....

Best Man ....

Church ....

....

....

Reception ....

....

Notes ....

....

....

....

....

> "There is no more lovely, friendly and charming relationship, communion or company than a good marriage."
> MARTIN LUTHER

Bride ....

Groom ....

Date ....

Bridesmaids / Matron of Honour

....
....
....

Best Man ....

Church ....

....
....

Reception ....

....

Notes ....

....
....
....
....

Photographs & Memories

Photographs & Memories

Weddings

Bride ....

Groom ....

Date ....

Bridesmaids / Matron of Honour

....

....

....

Best Man ....

Church ....

....

....

Reception ....

....

Notes ....

....

....

....

....

Weddings

Bride ....

Groom ....

     Date ....

     Bridesmaids / Matron of Honour

....

....

....

Best Man ....

Church ....

....

....

Reception ....

....

Notes ....

....

....

....

....

Photographs & Memories

Photographs & Memories

Religious Ceremonies

Name ....

Ceremony or Occasion ....
....

Date ....

Godparents or Sponsors ....

Place ....
....

Notes ....

~

Name ....

Ceremony or Occasion ....
....

Date ....

Godparents or Sponsors ....

Place ....
....

Notes ....

~

Name ....

Ceremony or Occasion ....
....

Date ....

Godparents or Sponsors ....

Place ....
....

Notes ....

> "God gave us memories that we might have roses in December."
> JAMES M BARRIE

Name ....

Ceremony or Occasion ....
....

Date ....
Godparents or Sponsors ....
Place ....
....
Notes ....

~

Name ....

Ceremony or Occasion ....
....

Date ....
Godparents or Sponsors ....
Place ....
....
Notes ....

~

Name ....

Ceremony or Occasion ....
....

Date ....
Godparents or Sponsors ....
Place ....
....
Notes ....

Religious Ceremonies

continued

Name ....

Ceremony or Occasion ....

....

Date ....

Godparents or Sponsors ....

Place ....

....

Notes ....

~

Name ....

Ceremony or Occasion ....

....

Date ....

Godparents or Sponsors ....

Place ....

....

Notes ....

~

Name ....

Ceremony or Occasion ....

....

Date ....

Godparents or Sponsors ....

Place ....

....

Notes ....

Name ....

Ceremony or Occasion ....

....

          Date ....

Godparents or Sponsors ....

Place ....

....

Notes ....

Name ....

Ceremony or Occasion ....

....

          Date ....

Godparents or Sponsors ....

Place ....

....

Notes ....

Name ....

Ceremony or Occasion ....

....

          Date ....

Godparents or Sponsors ....

Place ....

....

Notes ....

Education

Record information about the schools attended by your family members and any special achievements.

Name ....

Educational Establishment

....

....

Dates ....

Qualifications ....

....

Notes ....

~

Name ....

Educational Establishment

....

....

Dates ....

Qualifications ....

....

Notes ....

~

Name ....

Educational Establishment

....

....

Dates ....

Qualifications ....

....

Notes ....

"Education is what survives when what has been learnt has been forgotten."

B F SKINNER

Name ....

Educational Establishment

....

....

Dates ....

Qualifications ....

....

Notes ....

~

Name ....

Educational Establishment

....

....

Dates ....

Qualifications ....

....

Notes ....

~

Name ....

Educational Establishment

....

....

Dates ....

Qualifications ....

....

Notes ....

Education

Name ....

Educational Establishment

....

....

Dates ....

Qualifications ....

....

Notes ....

~

Name ....

Educational Establishment

....

....

Dates ....

Qualifications ....

....

Notes ....

~

Name ....

Educational Establishment

....

....

Dates ....

Qualifications ....

....

Notes ....

Name ....
Educational Establishment
....
....
Dates ....
Qualifications ....
....
Notes ....

~

Name ....
Educational Establishment
....
....
Dates ....
Qualifications ....
....
Notes ....

~

Name ....
Educational Establishment
....
....
Dates ....
Qualifications ....
....
Notes ....

Family Homes

The family home is a very memorable and important place.
Do you know when it was built? What improvements have you made?

Name of House..
  Address ....

....

....

Dates (from) .... to ....
Purchase Value ....
Sale Value ....
Notes ....

....

~

Name of House..
  Address ....

....

....

Dates (from) .... to ....
Purchase Value ....
Sale Value ....
Notes ....

....

~

Name of House..
  Address ....

....

....

Dates (from) .... to ....
Purchase Value ....
Sale Value ....
Notes ....

....

"The home of everyone is to him his castle and fortress, as well for his defence against injury and violence, as for his repose."

EDWARD COKE"

Name of House...

    Address ....

....

Dates (from) .... to ....

Purchase Value ....

Sale Value ....

Notes ....

....

~

Name of House...

    Address ....

....

Dates (from) .... to ....

Purchase Value ....

Sale Value ....

Notes ....

....

~

Name of House...

    Address ....

....

Dates (from) .... to ....

Purchase Value ....

Sale Value ....

Notes ....

....

Family Homes

Name of House...
  Address ....
....
....
Dates (from) .... to ....
Purchase Value ....
Sale Value ....
Notes ....
....

~

Name of House...
  Address ....
....
....
Dates (from) .... to ....
Purchase Value ....
Sale Value ....
Notes ....
....

~

Name of House...
  Address ....
....
....
Dates (from) .... to ....
Purchase Value ....
Sale Value ....
Notes ....
....

Name of House...
   Address ....
....
....
Dates (from) .... to ....
Purchase Value   ....
Sale Value   ....
Notes   ....
....

~

Name of House...
   Address ....
....
....
Dates (from) .... to ....
Purchase Value   ....
Sale Value   ....
Notes   ....
....

~

Name of House...
   Address ....
....
....
Dates (from) .... to ....
Purchase Value   ....
Sale Value   ....
Notes   ....
....

Family Vehicles

Does your family have a car, motorcycle or something more unusual?
What is the most unusual means of transport used by your family?

Owner..

Model ....

Colour...Year ....

Dates of Ownership...

Notes..

~

Owner..

Model ....

Colour...Year ....

Dates of Ownership...

Notes..

~

Owner..

Model ....

Colour...Year ....

Dates of Ownership...

Notes..

~

Owner..

Model ....

Colour...Year ....

Dates of Ownership...

Notes..

Owner..
Model ....
Colour...Year ....
Dates of Ownership...
Notes..

~

Owner..
Model ....
Colour...Year ....
Dates of Ownership...
Notes..

~

Owner..
Model ....
Colour...Year ....
Dates of Ownership...
Notes..

~

Owner..
Model ....
Colour...Year ....
Dates of Ownership...
Notes..

Family Vehicles

Owner..

Model ....

Colour...Year ....

Dates of Ownership...

Notes..

~

Owner..

Model ....

Colour...Year ....

Dates of Ownership...

Notes..

~

Owner..

Model ....

Colour...Year ....

Dates of Ownership...

Notes..

~

Owner..

Model ....

Colour...Year ....

Dates of Ownership...

Notes..

Family Notes

Family Pets

Describe your family pets. Do older family members recall their pets? What is the strangest pet that anyone has had?

Pet's Name ....
Type of Animal ....
Dates of Ownership ....
Notes ....

....

~

Pet's Name ....
Type of Animal ....
Dates of Ownership ....
Notes ....

....

~

Pet's Name ....
Type of Animal ....
Dates of Ownership ....
Notes ....

....

~

Pet's Name ....
Type of Animal ....
Dates of Ownership ....
Notes ....

....

Animals are such agreeable
friends – they ask no questions,
they pass no criticisms."
GEORGE ELIOT

Pet's Name ....
Type of Animal ....
Dates of Ownership ....
Notes ....

....

~

Pet's Name ....
Type of Animal ....
Dates of Ownership ....
Notes ....

....

~

Pet's Name ....
Type of Animal ....
Dates of Ownership ....
Notes ....

....

~

Pet's Name ....
Type of Animal ....
Dates of Ownership ....
Notes ....

....

Family Pets

Pet's Name ....

Type of Animal ....

Dates of Ownership ....

Notes ....

....

Pet's Name ....

Type of Animal ....

Dates of Ownership ....

Notes ....

....

Pet's Name ....

Type of Animal ....

Dates of Ownership ....

Notes ....

....

Pet's Name ....

Type of Animal ....

Dates of Ownership ....

Notes ....

....

Pet's Name ....

Type of Animal ....

Dates of Ownership ....

Notes ....

....

~

Pet's Name ....

Type of Animal ....

Dates of Ownership ....

Notes ....

....

~

Pet's Name ....

Type of Animal ....

Dates of Ownership ....

Notes ....

....

~

Pet's Name ....

Type of Animal ....

Dates of Ownership ....

Notes ....

....

Events to Remember

Event ....
Date ....
Notes ....
....
....

~

Event ....
Date ....
Notes ....
....
....

~

Event ....
Date ....
Notes ....
....
....

~

Event ....
Date ....
Notes ....
....
....

Event ....

Date ....

Notes ....

....

....

....

~

Event ....

Date ....

Notes ....

....

....

....

~

Event ....

Date ....

Notes ....

....

....

....

~

Event ....

Date ....

Notes ....

....

....

....

Events to Remember

continued

Event ....
Date ....
Notes ....
....
....
....

~

Event ....
Date ....
Notes ....
....
....
....

~

Event ....
Date ....
Notes ....
....
....
....

~

Event ....
Date ....
Notes ....
....
....
....

Event ....

Date ....

Notes ....

....

....

....

~

Event ....

Date ....

Notes ....

....

....

....

~

Event ....

Date ....

Notes ....

....

....

....

~

Event ....

Date ....

Notes ....

....

....

....

Reunions

Occasion ....

Date ....

Location ....

Who Attended ....

....

....

Notes ....

....

~

Occasion ....

Date ....

Location ....

Who Attended ....

....

....

....

Notes ....

....

~

Occasion ....

Date ....

Location ....

Who Attended ....

....

....

Notes ....

....

"A friend is a gift you
give yourself."

ROBERT LOUIS STEVENSON

Occasion ....

Date ....

Location ....

Who Attended ....

....

....

Notes ....

....

~

Occasion ....

Date ....

Location ....

Who Attended ....

....

....

Notes ....

....

~

Occasion ....

Date ....

Location ....

Who Attended ....

....

....

Notes ....

....

Reunions

continued

Occasion ....
Date ....
Location ....
Who Attended ....

....

....

Notes ....

....

~

Occasion ....
Date ....
Location ....
Who Attended ....

....

....

....

Notes ....

....

~

Occasion ....
Date ....
Location ....
Who Attended ....

....

....

....

Notes ....

....

Occasion ....
Date ....
Location ....
Who Attended ....

....

....

....

Notes ....

....

~

Occasion ....
Date ....
Location ....
Who Attended ....

....

....

....

Notes ....

....

~

Occasion ....
Date ....
Location ....
Who Attended ....

....

....

....

Notes ....

....

Family Holidays

Where ....
Dates ....
Location ....
Who was there ....

....

Notes ....

....

....

....

~

Where ....
Dates ....
Location ....
Who was there ....

....

Notes ....

....

....

....

~

Where ....
Dates ....
Location ....
Who was there ....

....

Notes ....

....

....

....

"What is this life if, full of care,
We have no time to
stand and stare?"
W H DAVIES

Where   ....
Dates   ....
Location   ....
Who was there ....
           ....
Notes   ....
....
....
....

~

Where   ....
Dates   ....
Location   ....
Who was there ....
           ....
Notes   ....
....
....
....

~

Where   ....
Dates   ....
Location   ....
Who was there ....
           ....
Notes   ....
....
....
....

Family Holidays

continued

Where ....
Dates ....
Location ....
Who was there ....
....
Notes ....
....
....
....

~

Where ....
Dates ....
Location ....
Who was there ....
....
Notes ....
....
....
....

~

Where ....
Dates ....
Location ....
Who was there ....
....
Notes ....
....
....
....

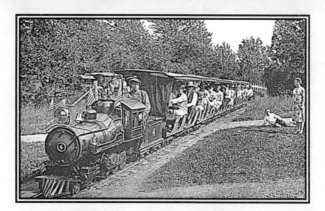

Where ....
Dates ....
Location ....
Who was there ....

....
Notes ....

....

....

....

~

Where ....
Dates ....
Location ....
Who was there ....

....
Notes ....

....

....

....

~

Where ....
Dates ....
Location ....
Who was there ....

Notes ....

....

....

....

Family Holidays

Where ....

Dates ....

Location ....

Who was there ....

....

Notes ....

....

....

....

~

Where ....

Dates ....

Location ....

Who was there ....

....

Notes ....

....

....

....

~

Where ....

Dates ....

Location ....

Who was there ....

....

Notes ....

....

....

....

Family Holidays

Where ....
Dates ....
Location ....
Who was there ....

....

Notes ....

....

....

~

Where ....
Dates ....
Location ....
Who was there ....

....

Notes ....

....

....

....

~

Where ....
Dates ....
Location ....
Who was there ....

....

Notes ....

....

....

....

Photographs &
Memories

Photographs & Memories

Illnesses

Name ....

Illness ....

Notes ....

....

....

....

~

Name ....

Illness ....

Notes ....

....

....

....

~

Name ....

Illness ....

Notes ....

....

....

....

~

Name ....

Illness ....

Notes ....

....

....

....

"I enjoy convalescence. It is the
part that makes the illness
worth while."
GEORGE BERNARD SHAW

Name ....

Illness ....

Notes ....

....

....

....

~

Name ....

Illness ....

Notes ....

....

....

....

~

Name ....

Illness ....

Notes ....

....

....

....

~

Name ....

Illness ....

Notes ....

....

....

....

Illnesses

Name ....
Illness ....
Notes ....

....
....
....

~

Name ....
Illness ....
Notes ....

....
....
....

~

Name ....
Illness ....
Notes ....

....
....
....

~

Name ....
Illness ....
Notes ....

....
....
....

Name ....

Illness ....

Notes ....

....

....

....

~

Name ....

Illness ....

Notes ....

....

....

....

~

Name ....

Illness ....

Notes ....

....

....

....

~

Name ....

Illness ....

Notes ....

....

....

....

Clubs & Organisations

Name ....
Club/Organisation...
....
Notes ....
....
....

~

Name ....
Club/Organisation...
....
Notes ....
....
....

~

Name ....
Club/Organisation...
....
Notes ....
....
....

~

Name ....
Club/Organisation...
....
Notes ....
....
....

> "I do not care to belong to a club that accepts people like me as members."
> GROUCHO MARX

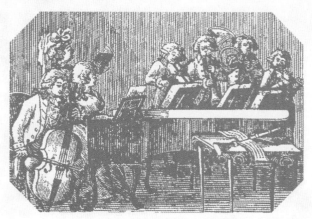

Name ....
Club/Organisation...
....
Notes ....
....
....

~

Name ....
Club/Organisation...
....
Notes ....
....
....

~

Name ....
Club/Organisation...
....
Notes ....
....
....

~

Name ....
Club/Organisation...
....
Notes ....
....
....

Clubs & Organisations

continued

Name ....

Club/Organisation ....

Notes ....

....

~

Name ....

Club/Organisation ....

Notes ....

....

~

Name ....

Club/Organisation ....

Notes ....

....

~

Name ....

Club/Organisation ....

Notes ....

....

Name ....
Club/Organisation...

Notes ....
....
....

Name ....
Club/Organisation...
....
Notes ....
....
....

Name ....
Club/Organisation...

Notes ....
....
....

Name ....
Club/Organisation...
....
Notes ....
....
....

Family Friends

Name ....
Address ....
....
Notes ....
....
....

~

Name ....
Address ....
....
Notes ....
....
....

~

Name ....
Address ....
....
Notes ....
....
....

~

Name ....
Address ....
....
Notes ....
....

> "The ornament of a house is the friends who frequent it."
> EMERSON

Name ....
Address ....
....
Notes ....
....
....

~

Name ....
Address ....
....
Notes ....
....
....

~

Name ....
Address ....
....
Notes ....
....
....

~

Name ....
Address ....
....
Notes ....
....
....

Family Friends

Name ....
Address ....
....
Notes ....
....
....

~

Name ....
Address ....
....
Notes ....
....
....

~

Name ....
Address ....
....
Notes ....
....
....

~

Name ....
Address ....
....
Notes ....
....
....

Family Friends

Name ....
Address ....
....
Notes ....
....
....

~

Name ....
Address ....
....
Notes ....
....
....

~

Name ....
Address ....
....
Notes ....
....
....

~

Name ....
Address ....
....
Notes ....
....
....

Embarrassing Stories

Are there any stories that have embarrassed a family member
or the whole family? Did they say something they didn't mean,
or did they do something strange or weird?

Family Traditions

Are there any traditions particular to your family?
Any special family celebrations, gatherings, stories or recipes that have
been passed down from generation to generation?

Family Hobbies

Name ....
Hobby ....
....
Notes ....
....
....

~

Name ....
Hobby ....
....
Notes ....
....
....

~

Name...
....
Hobby ....
....
Notes ....
....

~

Name...
....
Hobby ....
....
Notes ....
....
....

"To the art of working well a civilized race would add the art of playing well."
George Santayana

Name ....
Hobby ....
....
Notes ....
....
....

~

Name ....
Hobby ....
....
Notes ....
....
....

~

Name ....
....
Hobby ....
....
Notes ....
....
....

~

Name ....
....
Hobby ....
....
Notes ....
....
....

Family Hobbies

Name ....
Hobby ....
....
Notes ....
....
....

~

Name ....
Hobby ....
....
Notes ....
....
....

~

Name...
....
Hobby ....
....
Notes ....
....
....

~

Name...
....
Hobby ....
....
Notes ....
....
....

Name ....
Hobby ....
....
Notes ....
....
....

~

Name ....
Hobby ....
....
Notes ....
....
....

~

Name...
....
Hobby ....
....
Notes ....
....
....

~

Name...
....
Hobby ....
....
Notes ....
....
....

Family Sports

Name ....
Sport ....
....
Notes ....
....
....

~

Name ....
Sport ....
....
Notes ....
....
....

~

Name...
....
Sport ....
....
Notes ....
....

~

Name...
....
Sport ....
....
Notes ....
....
....

"Sports do not build character.
They reveal it."
HEYWOOD BROUN

Name ....
Sport ....
....
Notes ....
....
....

~

Name ....
Sport ....
....
Notes ....
....
....

~

Name ....
....
Sport ....
....
Notes ....
....
....

~

Name ....
....
Sport ....
....
Notes ....
....
....

Family Sports

continued

Name ....
Sport ....
....
Notes ....
....
....

~

Name ....
Sport ....
....
Notes ....
....
....

~

Name...
....
Sport ....
....
Notes ....
....
....

~

Name...
....
Sport ....
....
Notes ....
....
....

Name ....
Sport ....
....
Notes ....
....
....

~

Name ....
Sport ....
....
Notes ....
....
....

~

Name ....
....
Sport ....
....
Notes ....
....
....

~

Name ....
....
Sport ....
....
Notes ....
....
....

Family Collections
& Heirlooms

Name ....
Item ....
Notes ....
....
....

Name ....
Item ....
Notes ....
....
....

Name ....

Item ....
Notes ....
....
....

Name ....

Item ....
Notes ....
....
....

"Bliss in possession will not last;
Remembered joys are never past."
JAMES MONTGOMERY

Name ....
Item ....
Notes ....
....
....

Name ....
Item ....
Notes ....
....
....

Name...
....
Item ....
Notes ....
....
....

~

Name...
....
Item ....
Notes ....
....
....

Family Collections & Heirlooms

continued

Name ....
Item ....
Notes ....

....

....

Name ....
Item ....
Notes ....

....

....

Name...

Item ....
Notes ....

....

....

Name...

....

Item ....
Notes ....

....

....

Name ....
Item ....
Notes ....
....
....

Name ....
Item ....
Notes ....
....
....

Name...
....
Item ....
Notes ....
....
....

Name...
....
Item ....
Notes ....
....
....

Photographs & Memories

Photographs & Memories

Family Bereavements

Family Bereavements

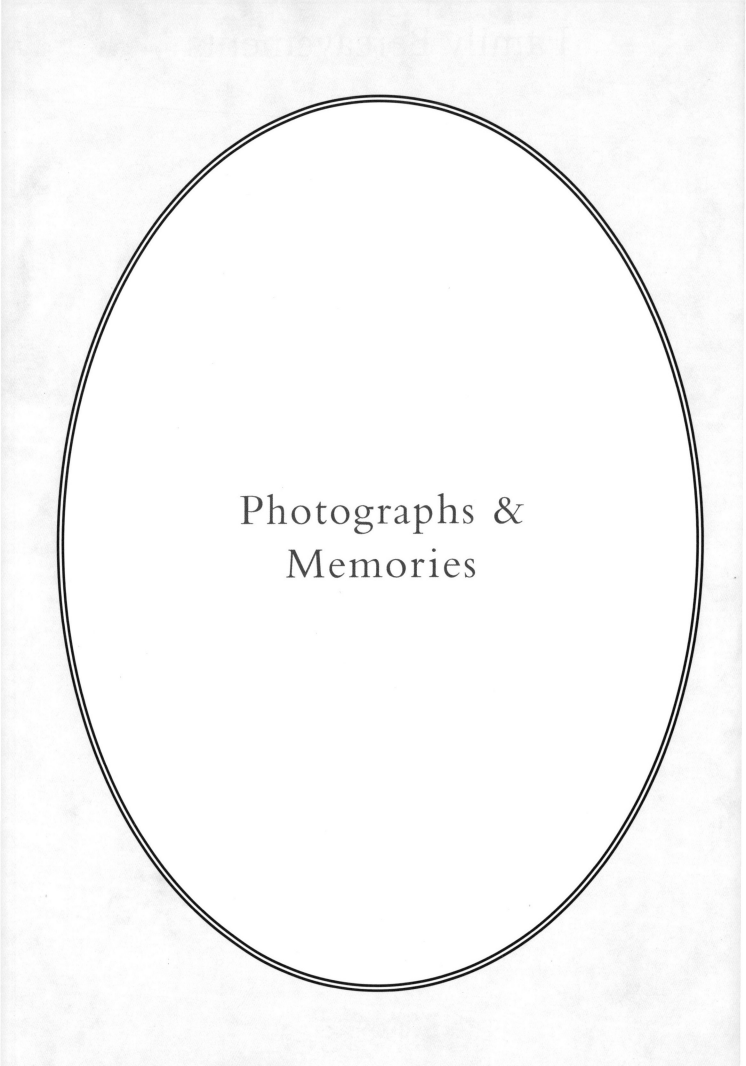

Photographs & Memories

Photographs & Memories

Husband's Great Great Grandfather's Name	Mr & Mrs	NEE
Husband's Great Great Grandmother's Name	Mr & Mrs	NEE
Husband's Great Great Grandfather's Name	Mr & Mrs	NEE
Husband's Great Great Grandmother's Name	Mr & Mrs	NEE
Husband's Great Great Grandfather's Name	Mr & Mrs	NEE
Husband's Great Great Grandmother's Name	Mr & Mrs	NEE
Husband's Great Great Grandfather's Name	Mr & Mrs	NEE
Husband's Great Great Grandmother's Name	Mr & Mrs	NEE
Husband's Great Great Grandfather's Name	Mr & Mrs	NEE
Husband's Great Great Grandmother's Name	Mr & Mrs	NEE
Husband's Great Great Grandfather's Name	Mr & Mrs	NEE
Husband's Great Great Grandmother's Name	Mr & Mrs	NEE
Husband's Great Great Grandfather's Name	Mr & Mrs	NEE
Husband's Great Great Grandmother's Name	Mr & Mrs	NEE
Husband's Great Great Grandfather's Name	Mr & Mrs	NEE
Husband's Great Great Grandmother's Name	Mr & Mrs	NEE
Wife's Great Great Grandfather's Name	Mr & Mrs	NEE
Wife's Great Great Grandmother's Name	Mr & Mrs	NEE
Wife's Great Great Grandfather's Name	Mr & Mrs	NEE
Wife's Great Great Grandmother's Name	Mr & Mrs	NEE
Wife's Great Great Grandfather's Name	Mr & Mrs	NEE
Wife's Great Great Grandmother's Name	Mr & Mrs	NEE
Wife's Great Great Grandfather's Name	Mr & Mrs	NEE
Wife's Great Great Grandmother's Name	Mr & Mrs	NEE
Wife's Great Great Grandfather's Name	Mr & Mrs	NEE
Wife's Great Great Grandmother's Name	Mr & Mrs	NEE
Wife's Great Great Grandfather's Name	Mr & Mrs	NEE
Wife's Great Great Grandmother's Name	Mr & Mrs	NEE
Wife's Great Great Grandfather's Name	Mr & Mrs	NEE
Wife's Great Great Grandmother's Name	Mr & Mrs	NEE
Wife's Great Great Grandfather's Name	Mr & Mrs	NEE
Wife's Great Great Grandmother's Name	Mr & Mrs	NEE